P9-DML-647

HENRY'S FREEDOM BOX

BY ELLEN LEVINE

ILLUSTRATED BY KADIR NELSON

SCHOLASTIC INC.
New York Toronto London Auckland Sydney
Mexico City New Delhi Hong Kong Buenos Aires

HENRY BROWN wasn't sure how old he was. Henry was a slave. And slaves weren't allowed to know their birthdays.

Henry and his brothers and sisters worked in the big house where the master lived. Henry's master had been good to Henry and his family.

But Henry's mother knew things could change. "Do you see those leaves blowing in the wind? They are torn from the trees like slave children are torn from their families."

One morning the master called for Henry and his mother. They climbed the wide staircase. The master lay in bed with only his head above the quilt. He was very ill. He beckoned them to come closer.

Some slaves were freed by their owners. Henry's heart beat fast. Maybe the master would set him free.

But the master said, "You are a good worker, Henry. I am giving you to my son. You must obey him and never tell a lie."

Henry nodded, but he didn't say thank you. That would have been a lie.

Later that day Henry watched a bird soar high above the trees. *Free bird! Happy bird!* Henry thought.

Henry said good-bye to his family. He looked across the field. The leaves swirled in the wind.

Henry worked in his new master's factory. He was good at his job.

"Do not tear that tobacco leaf!" the boss yelled at the new boy. He poked the boy with a stick.

If you made a mistake, the boss would beat you.

Henry was lonely. One day he met Nancy, who was shopping for her mistress.

They walked and talked and agreed to meet again. Henry felt like singing. But slaves didn't dare sing in the streets. Instead, he hummed all the way home.

Months later, Henry asked Nancy to be his wife. When both their masters agreed, Henry and Nancy were married.

Soon there was a little baby. Then another. And another.

Henry knew they were very lucky. They lived together even though they had different masters.

But Nancy was worried. Her master had lost a great deal of money. "I'm afraid he will sell our children," she said.

Henry sat very still.

Henry worked hard all morning.

He tried to forget what Nancy had said.

His friend James came into the factory. He whispered to Henry, "Your wife and children were just sold at the slave market."

"No!" cried Henry.

Henry couldn't move.

He couldn't think.

He couldn't work.

"Twist that tobacco!" The boss poked Henry.

Henry twisted tobacco leaves. His heart twisted in his chest.

At lunchtime, Henry rushed to the center of town. A large group of slaves was tied together. The owner shouted at them.

Henry looked for his family.

"Father! Father!"

Henry watched his children disappear down the road.

Where was Nancy?

He saw her the same moment she saw him.

When he wiped away his tears, Nancy, too, was gone.

F. G

Henry no longer sang. He couldn't hum.

He went to work, and at night he ate supper and went to bed.

Henry tried to think of happy times. But all he could see were the carts carrying away everyone he loved.

Henry knew he would never see his family again.

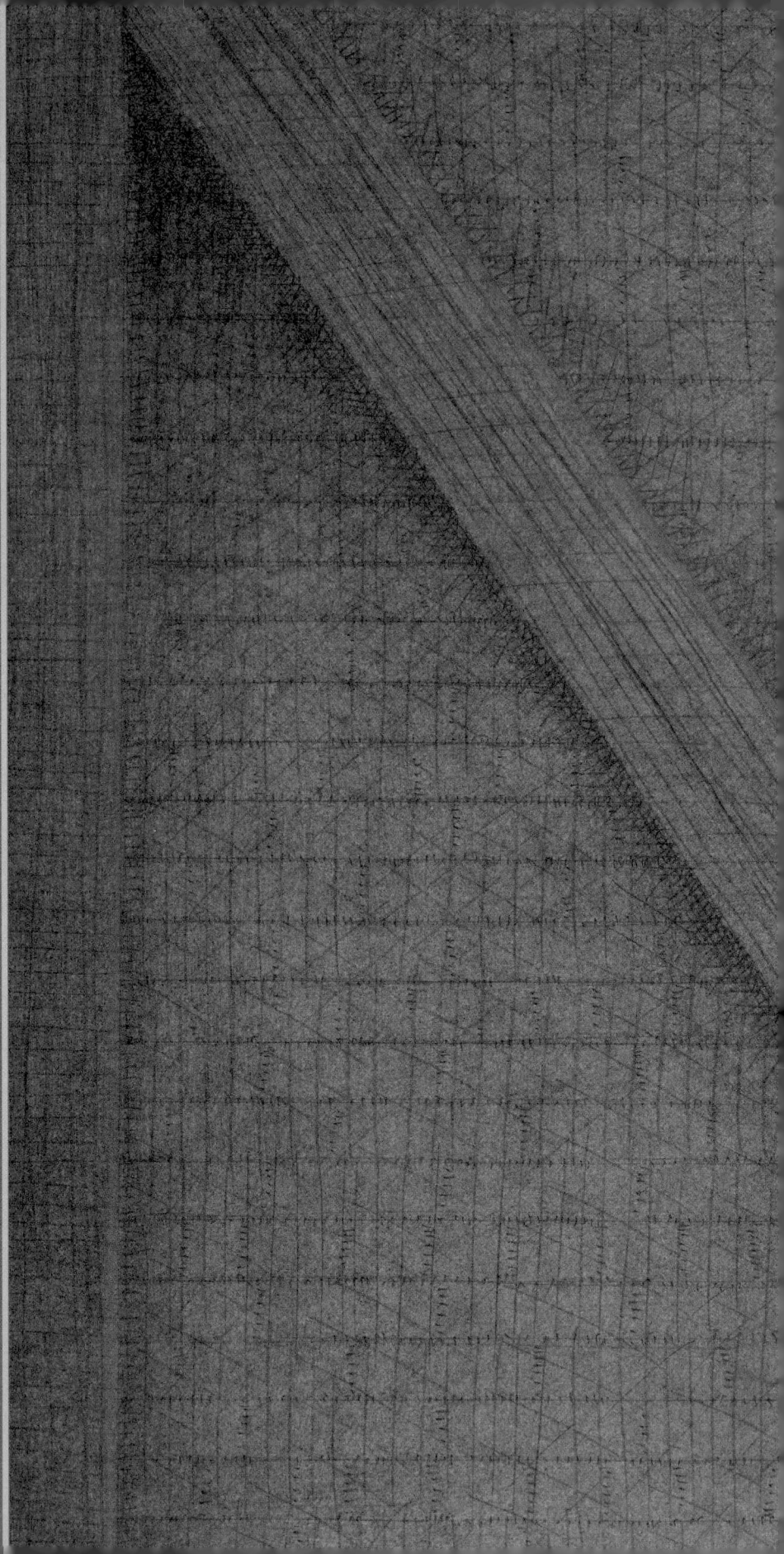

Many weeks passed. One morning, Henry heard singing. A little bird flew out of a tree into the open sky. And Henry thought about being free.

But how? As he lifted a crate, he knew the answer.

He asked James and Dr. Smith to help him. Dr. Smith was a white man who thought slavery was wrong.

They met early the next day at an empty warehouse.

Henry arrived with a box.

"I will mail myself to a place where there are no slaves!" he said.

James stared at the box, then at Henry. "What if you cough and someone hears you?"

"I will cover my mouth and hope," Henry said.

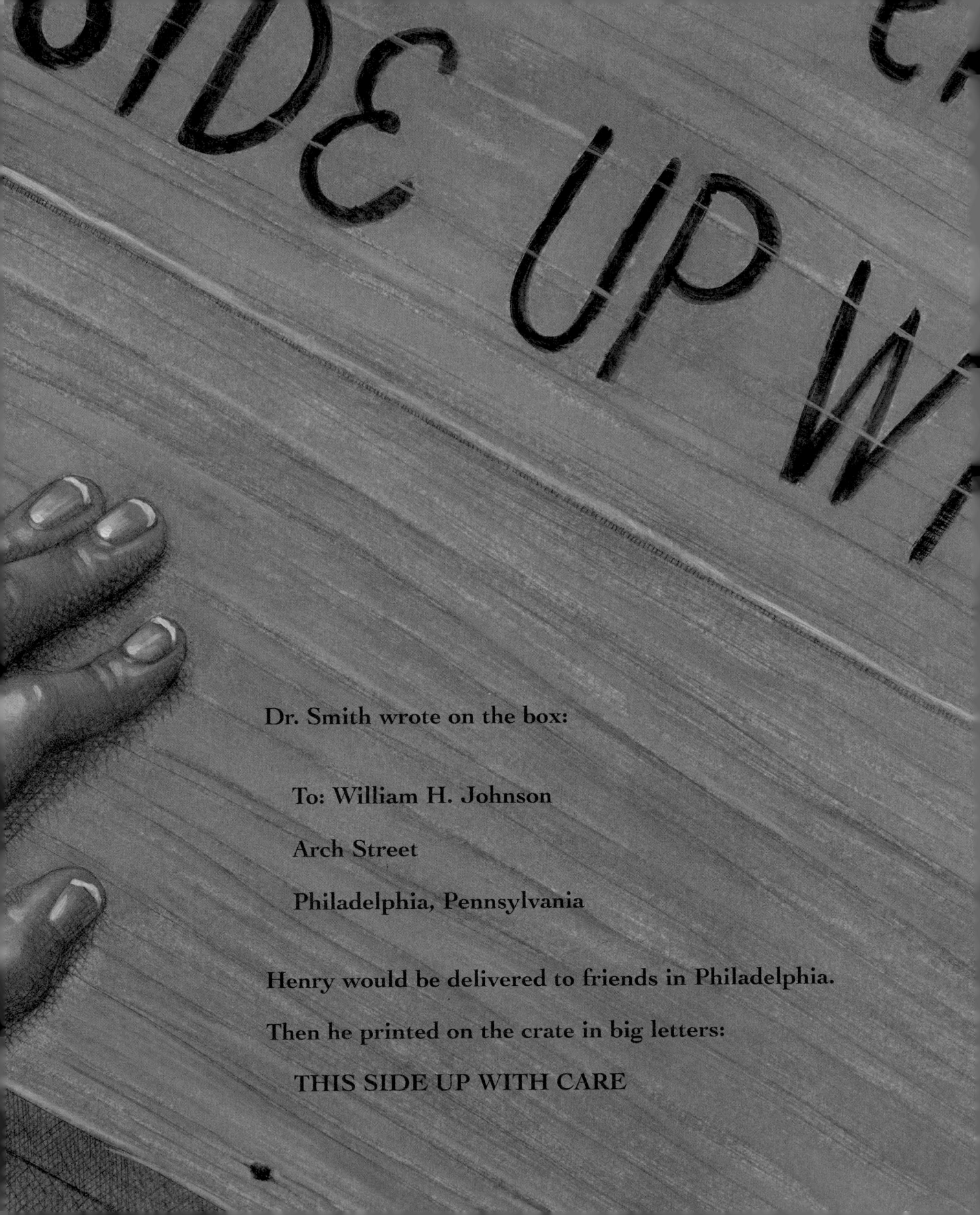

Dr. Smith wrote on the box:

To: William H. Johnson

Arch Street

Philadelphia, Pennsylvania

Henry would be delivered to friends in Philadelphia.

Then he printed on the crate in big letters:

THIS SIDE UP WITH CARE

nsylvania
Th

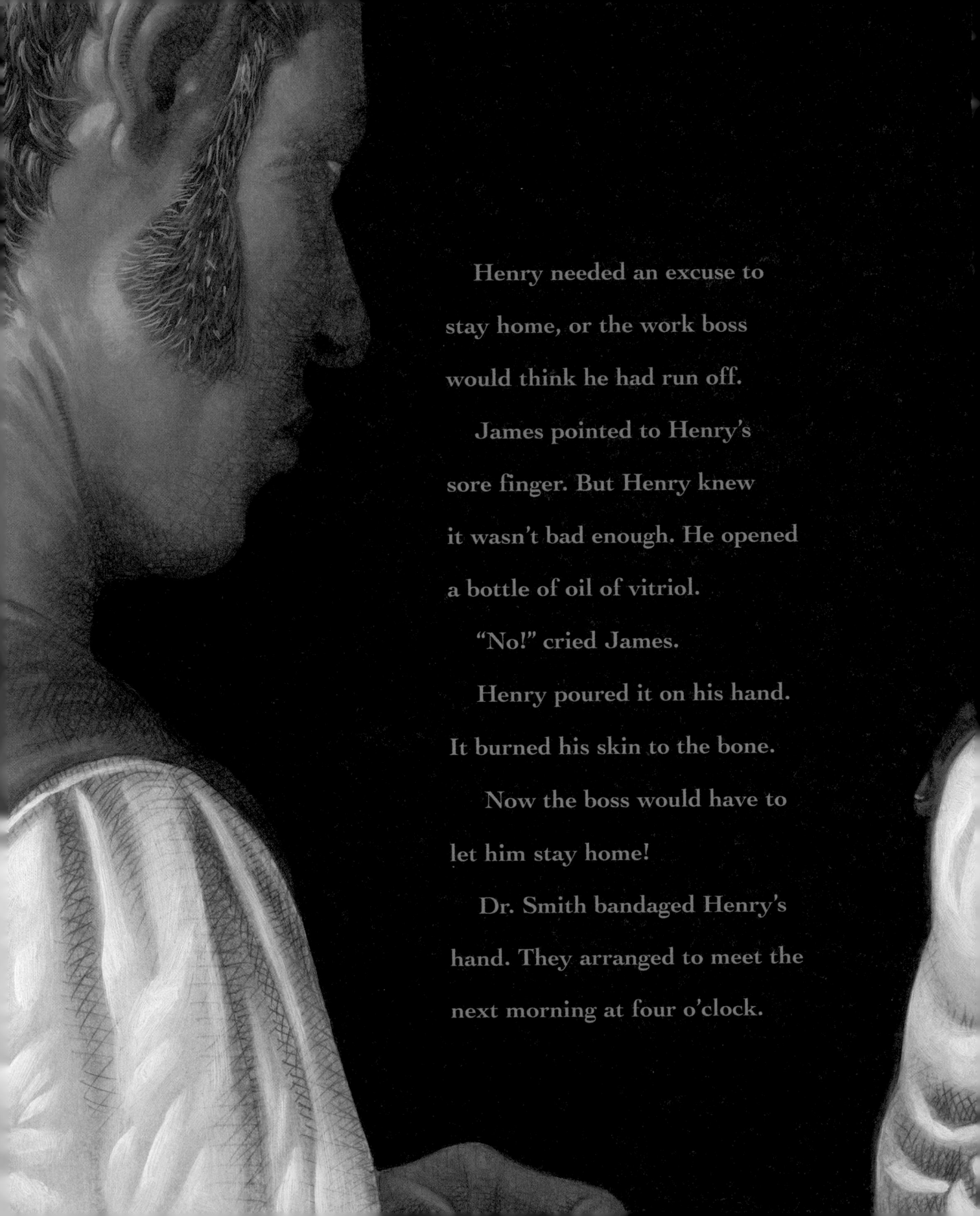

Henry needed an excuse to stay home, or the work boss would think he had run off.

James pointed to Henry's sore finger. But Henry knew it wasn't bad enough. He opened a bottle of oil of vitriol.

"No!" cried James.

Henry poured it on his hand. It burned his skin to the bone.

Now the boss would have to let him stay home!

Dr. Smith bandaged Henry's hand. They arranged to meet the next morning at four o'clock.

The sun was not yet up when Henry climbed into the box.

"Ready!" he said.

James nailed down the lid.

Dr. Smith and James drove to the station. The railway clerk tipped the box over and nailed a paper to the bottom.

Dr. Smith begged the clerks to be careful. But they didn't listen. They threw the box into the baggage car.

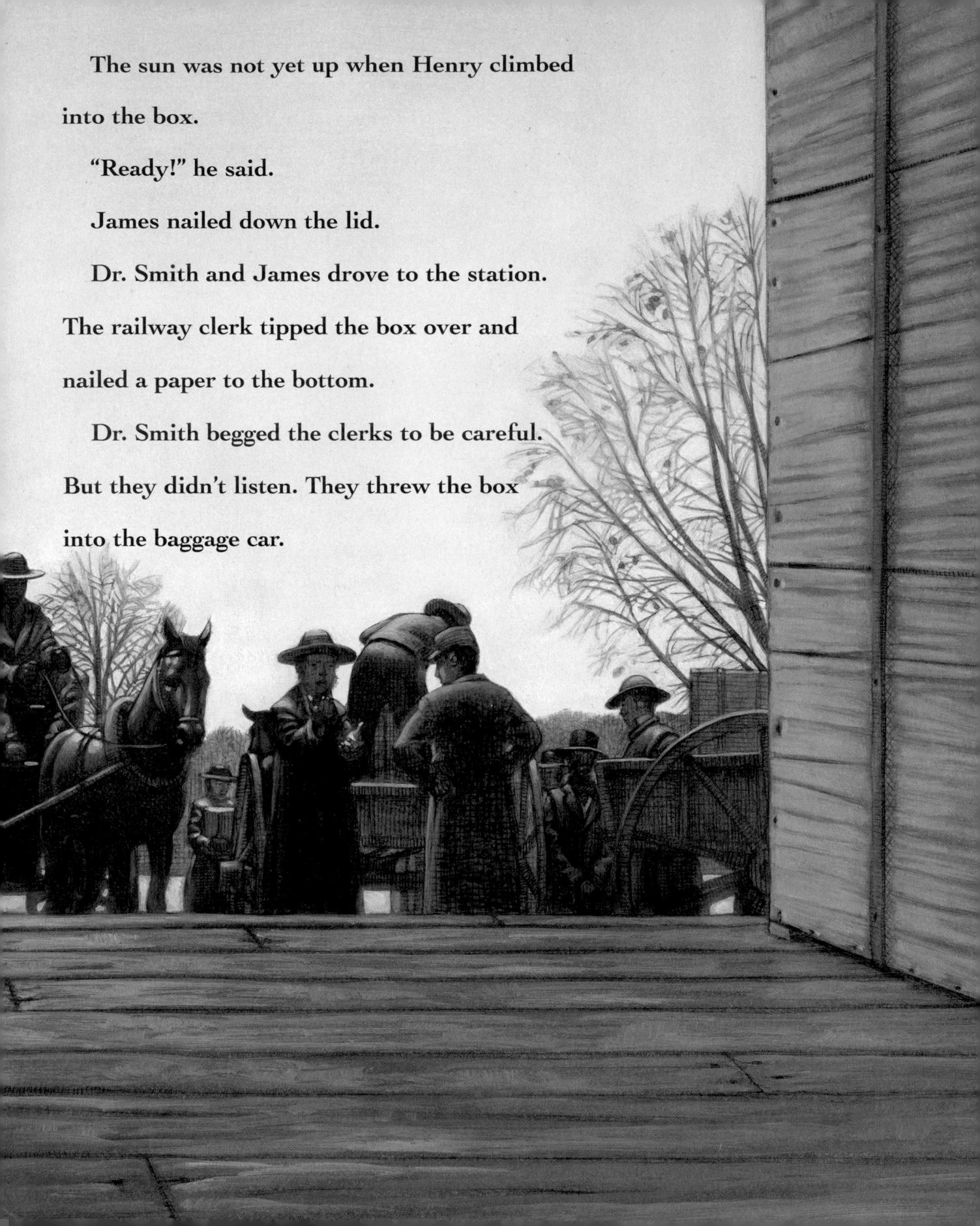

Philadel
THIS SI

Hours passed.

Henry was lifted up and thrown again.

Upside down!

He heard waves splashing. This must be the steamboat headed for Washington, D.C.

The ship rode smoothly, but Henry was still upside down.

Blood rushed to his head.

His face got hot.

His eyes ached.

He thought his head would burst.

But he was afraid to move. Someone might hear him.

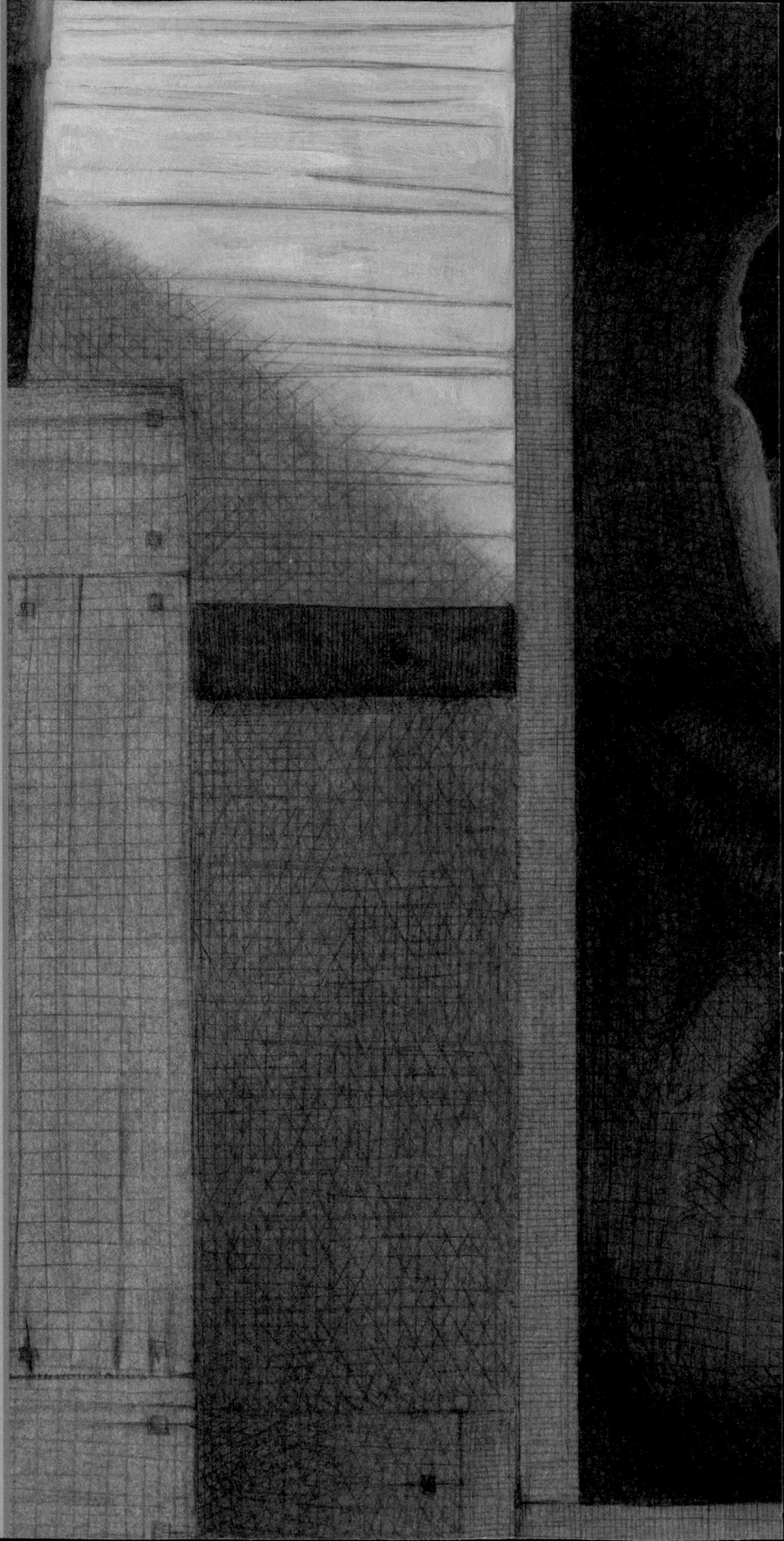

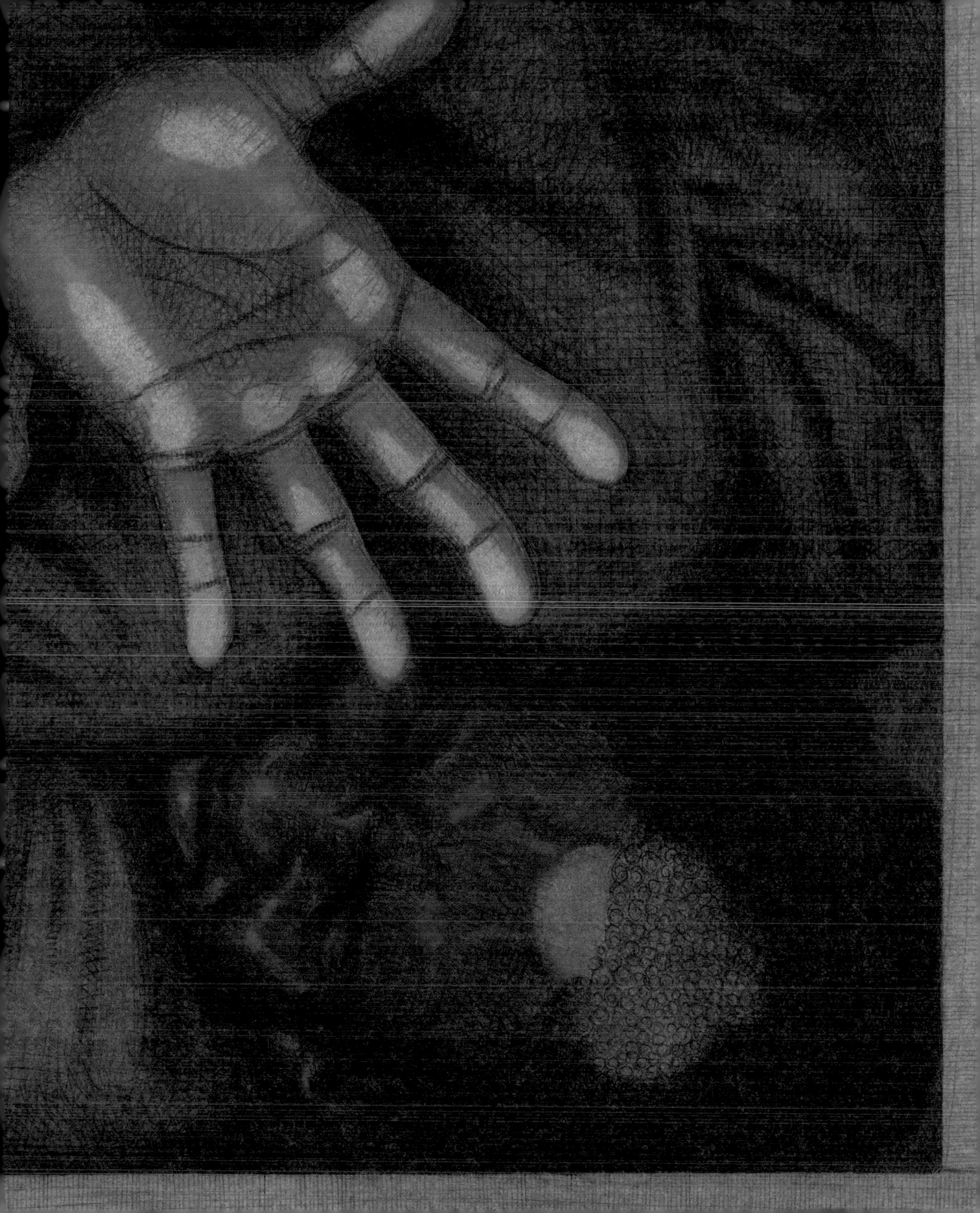

"I'm tired of standing,"

someone said.

"Why don't we move that box and sit on it?" said another.

Henry held his breath. Could they be talking about *his* box?

Henry was pushed.

The box scraped the deck.

Now he was on his right side!

Now on his left!

And suddenly, right side up!

"What do you think is in here?" said the first man.

"Mail, I guess," said the other.

I am *mail,* thought Henry.

But not the kind they imagine!

Henry was carried off the steamboat and placed in a railroad car, this time head up. He fell asleep to the rattling song of the train wheels.